the
Christopher Norton

CONCERT COLLECTION

for Flute

BOOSEY & HAWKES

CHRISTOPHER NORTON

Christopher Norton was born in New Zealand in 1953. After graduating he began his career as a teacher, pianist and composer, and began to develop an interest in popular music. Coming to the UK in 1977 on a university scholarship, he studied composition at York University with Wilfred Mellers and David Blake. Well established as a composer, producer, arranger and educationalist, Norton has written stage musicals, ballet scores, piano music, popular songs and orchestral music as well as jingles and signature tunes for TV and radio. He has lectured all over the world on aspects of his work and likes to integrate traditional teaching methods with aspects of modern technology.

Chris is best known for his world-famous series *Microjazz* — easy graded pieces in modern styles such as blues, rock 'n' roll, reggae and jazz — and for his award-winning *Essential Guides* to Pop Styles, Latin Styles and Jazz Styles. He has also created the *Micromusicals* series – short curriculum-linked musicals for children aged 5-11.

www.christophernorton.com

Published by Boosey & Hawkes Music Publishers Ltd
Aldwych House
71–91 Aldwych
London
WC2B 4HN

www.boosey.com

© Copyright 2022 by Boosey & Hawkes Music Publishers Ltd

ISMN 979-0-060-13855-3
ISBN 978-1-78454-671-7

First published 2006

Printed by Halstan:
Halstan UK, 2-10 Plantation Road, Amersham, Bucks, HP6 6HJ. United Kingdom
Halstan DE, Weißliliengasse 4, 55116 Mainz. Germany

Cover design by Chloë Alexander Design (www.chloealexanderdesign.com)
Music setting by Robin Hagues
Flute – Nicola Hunter
Piano – Christopher Norton
Track arrangements by Andy Green and Frank Mizen
Mastered by Richard Kimmings

the
Christopher Norton
CONCERT COLLECTION
for Flute

Improvisations on Spirituals

Improvisations on Folksongs

Inventions on best-loved Classical themes

Improvisations on songs by Stephen Foster

AUDIO RESOURCES

Stream or download audio for this book via the web address below or scan the QR code.

https://audio.boosey.com/fD7Z

1. Nobody knows

Christopher Norton

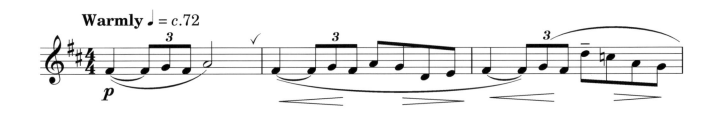

2. Swing low

Christopher Norton

3. Were you there?

Christopher Norton

6

4. Didn't my Lord deliver Daniel?

Christopher Norton

5. All through the night

Christopher Norton

6. Barbara Allen

Christopher Norton

7. Drunken sailor

Christopher Norton

8. John Peel on holiday

Christopher Norton

the
Christopher Norton
CONCERT COLLECTION
for Flute

Christopher Norton

Piano accompaniment

BOOSEY & HAWKES

CHRISTOPHER NORTON

Christopher Norton was born in New Zealand in 1953. After graduating he began his career as a teacher, pianist and composer, and began to develop an interest in popular music. Coming to the UK in 1977 on a university scholarship, he studied composition at York University with Wilfred Mellers and David Blake. Well established as a composer, producer, arranger and educationalist, Norton has written stage musicals, ballet scores, piano music, popular songs and orchestral music as well as jingles and signature tunes for TV and radio. He has lectured all over the world on aspects of his work and likes to integrate traditional teaching methods with aspects of modern technology.

Chris is best known for his world-famous series *Microjazz* — easy graded pieces in modern styles such as blues, rock 'n' roll, reggae and jazz — and for his award-winning *Essential Guides* to Pop Styles, Latin Styles and Jazz Styles. He has also created the *Micromusicals* series – short curriculum-linked musicals for children aged 5-11.

www.christophernorton.com

Published by Boosey & Hawkes Music Publishers Ltd
Aldwych House
71–91 Aldwych
London
WC2B 4HN

www.boosey.com

© Copyright 2022 by Boosey & Hawkes Music Publishers Ltd

ISMN 979-0-060-13855-3
ISBN 978-1-78454-671-7

First published 2006

Printed by Halstan:
Halstan UK, 2-10 Plantation Road, Amersham, Bucks, HP6 6HJ. United Kingdom
Halstan DE, Weißliliengasse 4, 55116 Mainz. Germany

Cover design by Chloë Alexander Design (www.chloealexanderdesign.com)
Music setting by Robin Hagues
Flute – Nicola Hunter
Piano – Christopher Norton
Track arrangements by Andy Green and Frank Mizen
Mastered by Richard Kimmings

the
Christopher Norton
CONCERT
COLLECTION
for Flute

Piano accompaniment

AUDIO RESOURCES

Stream or download audio for this book via the web address below or scan the QR code.

https://audio.boosey.com/fD7Z

1. Nobody knows

Christopher Norton

3

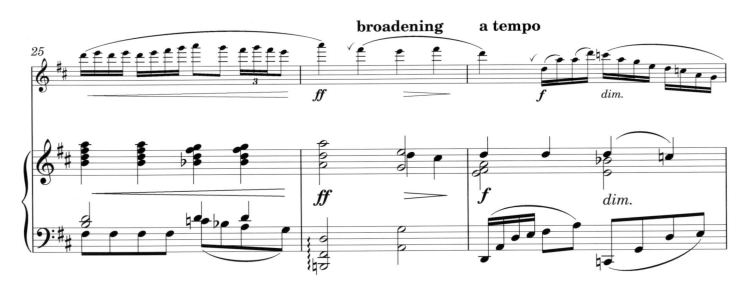

Gradually broadening to the end

2. Swing low

Christopher Norton

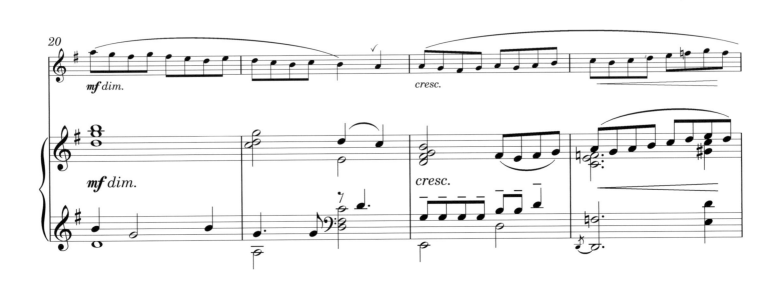

Slightly slowing

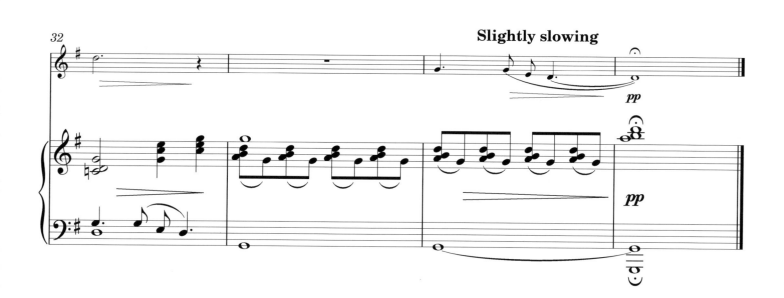

3. Were you there?

Christopher Norton

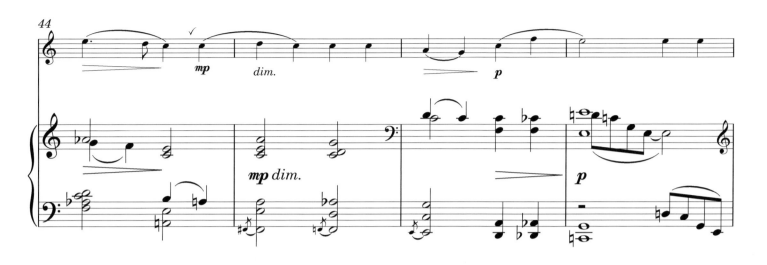

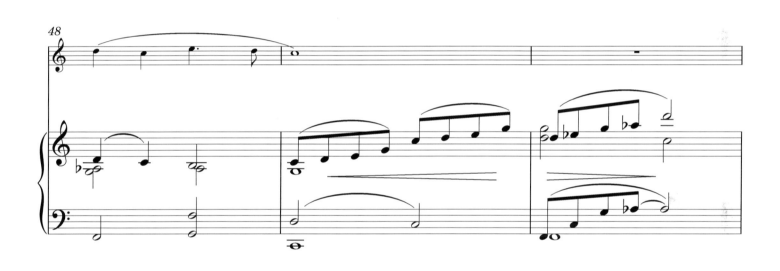

Slower **Much slower**

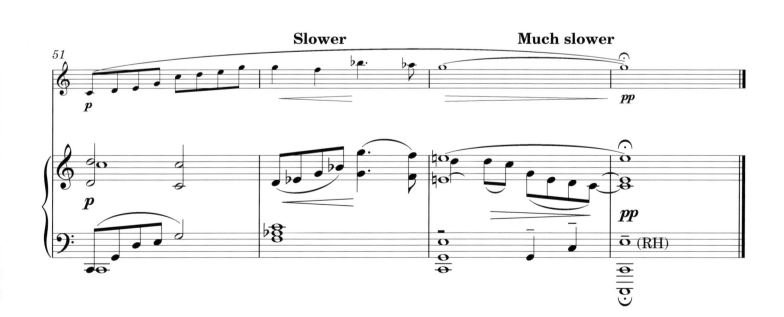

4. Didn't my Lord deliver Daniel?

Christopher Norton

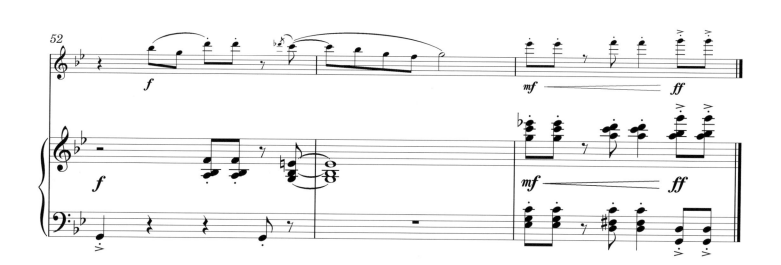

5. All through the night

Christopher Norton

6. Barbara Allen

Christopher Norton

7. Drunken sailor

Christopher Norton

8. John Peel on holiday

Christopher Norton

9. A Latin Musical Joke

Christopher Norton
after Mozart

10. Seville stomp

Christopher Norton
after Rossini

11. The young huntsman

Christopher Norton
after Schumann

In a spirited fashion ♩ = 116

12. Dream of love

Christopher Norton
after Liszt

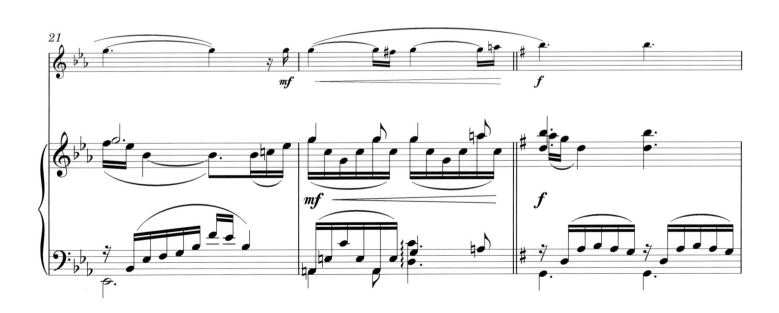

13. Susanna at the hoedown

Christopher Norton
after Stephen Foster

14. Beautiful dreamer

Christopher Norton
after Stephen Foster

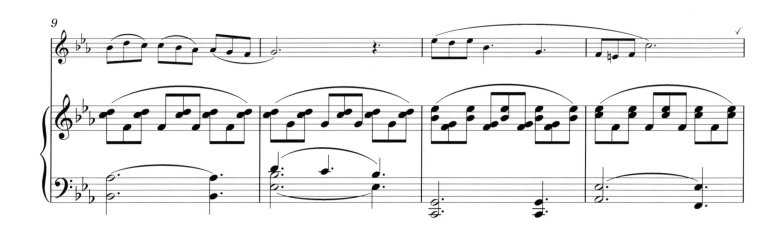

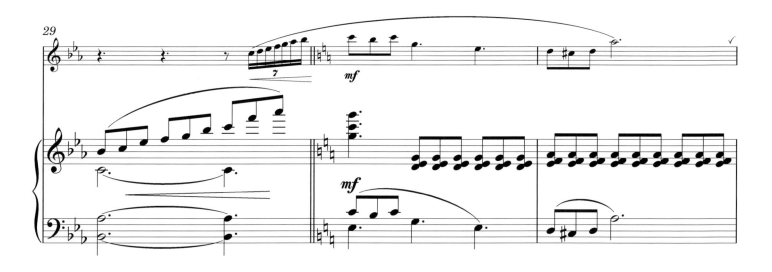

poco rit.   a tempo

Slowing

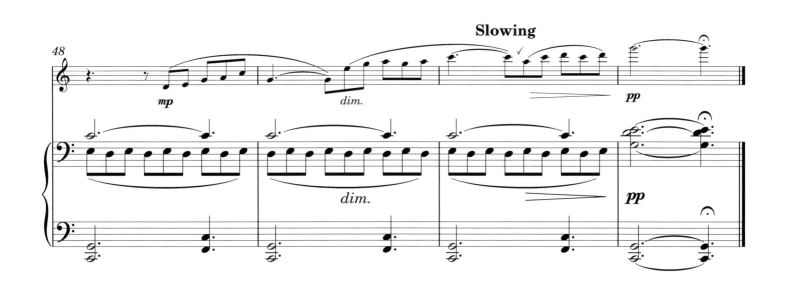

15. I dream of Jeannie

Christopher Norton
after Stephen Foster

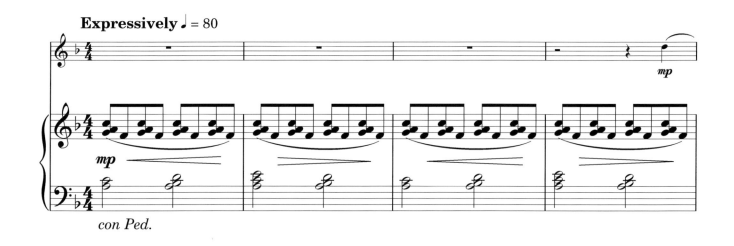

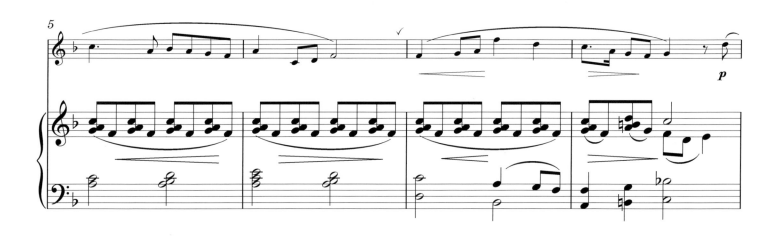

9. A Latin Musical Joke

Christopher Norton
after Mozart

10. Seville stomp

Christopher Norton
after Rossini

11. The young huntsman

Christopher Norton
after Schumann

12. Dream of love

Christopher Norton
after Liszt

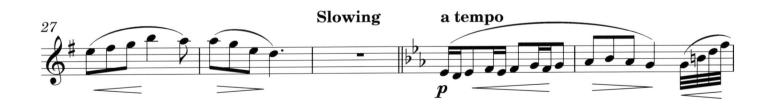

Slowing to the end

13. Susanna at the hoedown

Christopher Norton
after Stephen Foster

14. Beautiful dreamer

Christopher Norton
after Stephen Foster

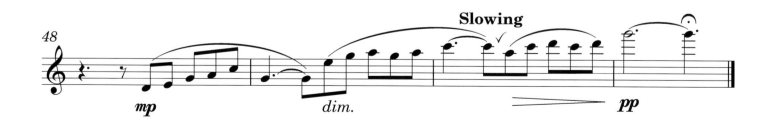

15. I dream of Jeannie

Christopher Norton
after Stephen Foster